KU-120-300

Exposure to radon

The Ionising Radiations Regulations 1985

Health and Safety Commission

WS
350
HEA

Approved Code of Practice

A06865

London: Her Majesty's Stationery Office

General enquiries regarding this publication should be
addressed to the Health and Safety Executive at any of the
following public enquiry points:

Library and Information Services
Broad Lane
SHEFFIELD S3 7HQ
Telephone: (0742) 752539 Telex: 54556

Library and Information Services
St Hugh's House
Stanley Precinct
Trinity Road
BOOTLE
Merseyside L20 3QY
Telephone: 051-951 4381 Telex: 628235

Library and Information Services
Baynards House
1 Chepstow Place
Westbourne Grove
LONDON W2 4TF
Telephone: 01-221 0870
Telex: 25683

ISBN 0 11 883978 0

Contents

Notice of Approval   By virtue of Section 16(1) of the Health and Safety at Work etc Act 1974 and with the consent of the Secretary of State for Employment the Health and Safety Commission has on 5 October 1987 approved the Code of Practice *Exposure to Radon*.

The Code of Practice is approved for the purpose of providing practical guidance with respect to the Ionising Radiations Regulations 1985.

The Code of Practice comes into effect on 4 April 1988.

Signed

A J LORD
Secretary to the Health and Safety Commission

Introduction

1   This is the third part of the Approved Code of Practice which was envisaged when the Health and Safety Commission approved Parts 1 and 2 on 3 September 1985. This part has now been approved by the Health and Safety Commission (HSC) with the consent of the Secretary of State under section 16 of the Health and Safety at Work etc Act 1974 (HSW Act) for the purpose of providing practical guidance with respect to the provisions of the Ionising Radiations Regulations 1985 (SI No 1333).

2   Part 3 gives specific guidance on the application of the Regulations to certain work involving exposure to isotopes of radon and their decay products. It has been drawn up following consultation with interested parties and in particular with a Working Group comprising nominees from the Confederation of British Industry (CBI) and the Trades Union Congress (TUC), together with independent technical experts and representatives of the Health and Safety Executive (HSE). The National Radiological Protection Board (NRPB) has also been consulted (as required by section 16(2) of the HSW Act) and its advice has been incorporated in the Code of Practice.

3   The provisions of the Code represent, in the opinion of HSC, the most appropriate methods of complying with the regulatory requirements and, in particular, the methods which should be considered to be reasonably practicable when that term appears in the Regulations.

4   Although failure to observe any provision of this part of the Code is not in itself an offence, that failure may be taken by a Court in criminal proceedings as proof that a person has contravened the Regulation to which the provision relates. In such a case, however, it will be open to that person to satisfy the Court that he has complied with the Regulation in some other way.

5   Words and expressions which are defined in the HSW Act, the Mines and Quarries Act 1954 or in the Ionising Radiations Regulations 1985 have the same meaning in this Code unless the context requires otherwise. Any reference in this Code to any publication does not imply approval by HSC of that publication or any part of it as an Approved Code of Practice except to the extent necessary to give effect to this Code.

6   A reference in this Code to radon means gaseous radon 222 and a reference to radon daughters means the short lived daughters of radon 222 as defined in Regulation 2(1), unless the context requires otherwise.

7   The information in this part of the code is additional to that given in Part 1 and should be read in conjunction with the latter and with the Regulations. Part 3 applies when there is exposure of persons to the short lived daughters of radon 222 above an energy concentration in air of 6.24×10^{-7} Jm^{-3} (0.03 WL), (see Regulation 2(1) and paragraph 13).

8   Workplaces where such exposure may occur include:

(a)   any working mine;

(b)   tourist mines and caverns;

(c)   other underground workplaces including civil engineering works; and

(d)   ground level workplaces and basements where radon can accumulate after permeating to the surface from underlying rock containing uranium. Places where this is most likely to occur are in certain parts of Cornwall and Devon.

No places above ground floor levels and no large industrial workplaces at ground level have been found with radon daughter concentrations above the level quoted in paragraph 7.

9   Radon 222 is a radioactive gaseous product in the naturally occurring uranium 238 decay series. It is formed in any material containing uranium and can subsequently permeate into the air of a workplace. Its own decay in air gives rise to a series of particulate short lived decay products known as daughters, which if

inhaled and retained in the lung may cause a risk to health.

10 Where employers have reason to believe that exposure to radon and/or its daughters may be significant in a particular workplace they should seek advice from a radiation protection service or from HSE.

11 The guidance in this document is based on techniques and knowledge current at the time of publication.

PART 3

**REGULATION 6
Restriction of
exposure**

1   The control measures and advice in pargraphs 2 to 5 mainly relate to operations in mines. However, some of these measures will apply to other situations eg in tunnels, cellars, underground facilities or buildings where there is exposure to radon daughters. In particular the provision of ventilation to dilute or reduce the build up of radon and by ageing radon daughter concentrations and sealing to prevent the ingress of radon are likely to be relevant. The employer should choose the control measures necessary to comply with the requirements of Regulation 6 after consultation with his radiation protection adviser.

2   Exposure to radon daughters can be controlled by:

(a)   minimising the entry of radon into a workplace;

(b)   ventilation; or

(c)   limiting the duration of exposure.

Paragraphs 3 to 6 describe control measures in each group.

3   The following are examples of controlling radon at source:

(a)   in mines, sealing old and unused areas (including boreholes) from working areas to minimise leakage into ventilation circuits;

(b)   planning and laying out the mine to minimise contact with old workings;

(c)   minimising the area of exposed rock;

(d)   preventing or minimising the release of radon gas from water entering mine workings by piping water with high radon content from point of entry to discharge, and by avoiding water turbulence in intake airways or at occupied locations (it should be borne in mind that dissolved radon gas is very rapidly released from water after contact with mine air);

(e)   reducing the contamination of air by not locating crushing and tipping plant in intake airways. This source of radon is less significant than many others but may nevertheless have an effect on radon concentrations;

(f)   sealing walls or floor surfaces in buildings, lined tunnels and other similar places.

4   Ventilation control is a primary means of reducing radon daughter concentrations. Working places not in through ventilation airways eg working places in blind ends in mines, should be provided with auxiliary ventilation. It is worth noting that dust control achieved by filtration may help control radon daughter levels; other techniques such as wetting, while valuable and necessary in controlling dust levels, do not appear to have much effect on concentrations of either radon or radon daughters.

5   Ventilation systems should be designed to:

(a)   avoid the use of shafts and workings contaminated with radon as intake airways;

(b)   minimise the amount of contaminated air drawn through old workings into air intakes or ventilation circuits;

(c)   minimise the residence time of air in the ventilation system;

(d)   take account of the likelihood of increasing contamination by aggregation in series ventilation systems;

(e)   avoid polluting intake air by return air;

(f)   minimise the effect of failure of main fans. Unmanned surface or booster fans should be provided with an alarm system to indicate failure;

(g)   make best use of the effects of pressure balancing;

(h) make best use of double door systems as airlocks to help maintain pressure balance;

(i) provide a separate supply of uncontaminated air at the location of strong sources of radon (eg at crusher stations and pump rooms etc.);

(j) avoid creating a negative pressure gradient between occupied space in a building and soil gas. Increasing the ventilation to the extent that this effect occurs can draw in more radon and outweigh any advantage.

6 Employers can also exercise working controls on limiting exposure such as those included in local rules and written systems of work. However, the primary method for restricting exposure should be by means of engineering controls.

7 Personal respiratory protection should not be considered as part of the normal control measures of the mine. Such equipment should be provided for emergency use in the event of ventilation failures or where initial entry into contaminated areas is necessary before ventilation can be established.

8 Employers should ensure that radon daughters in upcast air discharged from any underground workplace does not cause undue exposure. If either the concentration of radon daughters is high or the immediate vicinity is occupied then measurements should be made to check that the necessary restriction of exposure is being achieved.

REGULATION 7
Dose limits

9 The common measurement quantity for radon daughters is the potential alpha energy concentration in the air. This quantity can be expressed in joules per cubic metre (Jm^{-3}) or more commonly in the special unit, the working level (WL) (1 WL = 2.08×10^{-5} Jm^{-3}). Exposure to radon daughters is commonly expressed in units of working level month (WLM). An exposure of 1 WLM can be taken to be received by a person working in a radon daughter concentration of 1 WL for 170 hours. Expressed another way:

Exposure in WLM = $\dfrac{WL \times h}{170}$ where h is the time of exposure in hours.

For the purpose of the Regulations exposure to 4.8 WLM of radon daughters gives rise to a committed dose which equates to a committed effective dose equivalent of 50 mSv. This is the annual (whole body) dose limit for employees aged 18 years and over.

10 When there is occupational exposure to radon daughters there will normally be additional exposure to other associated naturally occurring radiation. This arises almost entirely from:

(a) exposure to the daughters of radon 220 (thoron);

(b) gamma radiation from the decay of potassium 40, and some radionuclides in the uranium 238 and thorium 232 series; and

(c) the intake of the long-lived radionuclides of the uranium and thorium decay series.

This is particularly relevant in underground mines and caverns.

11 A dose assessment should include the sum of doses from all sources associated with the occupational exposure. To simplify monitoring procedures, if a practical exposure limit of 4 WLM is used instead of the 4.8 WLM described in paragraph 9 then only the exposure to radon daughters need be assessed, rather than that from all the sources of natural radiation mentioned in paragraph 10. The difference of 0.8 WLM is an adequate allowance in the United Kingdom for the occupational exposure to all other natural radiation (see Appendix 1). It does not, however, cater for any dose arising from other work with ionising radiations eg sealed sources and X-ray equipment.

REGULATION 8
Controlled areas

12 Part IV of Schedule 6 to the Regulations, rather than Part II, gives criteria for determining and designating controlled areas when there is exposure to radon daughters. In ground level workplaces, the steps taken to comply with Regulation 6 would normally be expected to restrict the air concentration of radon daughters below the point where controlled or supervised areas need to be designated. This may not be possible in many underground workplaces and in these cases the following guidance applies.

13 For the purposes of comparison with the level specified in Part IV of Schedule 6, 2×10^{-6} J/m^3 (0.1 WL), the potential alpha energy concentration should be the average value of measurements taken at that place over any continuous 8 hour working period during any part of which an employee may enter.

14 The size of a controlled area may range from one specified part of a workplace to the whole of it, eg, for a mine it could involve designation of the whole mine or, in some cases, only individual places of work. For managerial control of access, some employers may wish to designate certain sections of the workplace even though it is clear that concentrations within those areas do not exceed 0.1 WL (the figure above which an employer is required to designate an area, see Regulation 8 and Part IV of Schedule 6).

15 After the extent of a controlled area has been established, the boundary should be clearly marked to ensure that people are aware of its designation. In most cases convenient boundaries that exist for reasons other than radiation protection may be used (see paragraph 14). In the case of a mine, a warning notice should be placed at each entry point stating that entry to the controlled area is restricted to classified persons and to those operating under a written system of work.

16 A written system of work may allow people who are not classified persons to enter a controlled area, provided that certain conditions are observed (see Regulations 8(6) and (7) and paragraphs 49 to 54 of Part 1 of this Code). This approach is particularly relevant when the whole of a mine, cellar or underground facility has been designated as a controlled area and entry is required by:

(a) a person who is only likely to enter for a very limited period, eg a visitor; or

(b) any other person who regularly visits or works in parts where it is known that concentrations are below 0.1 WL.

In demonstrating that the doses are restricted as required by Regulation 8(7), personal dosemeters should be used or alternatively the time spent in the area and the exposure levels should be recorded. Records should be kept for at least the following calendar year. Where it is clear that the time spent in the controlled area in a year is negligible eg a visitor sightseeing in a tourist cave, then a knowledge of the average dose received on a typical visit should suffice (see paragraph 19).

REGULATION 10
Radiation protection advisers (RPA)

17 The functions of the RPA as described in paragraphs 68 to 76 of Part 1 of the Code do not include a need for giving advice on ventilation engineering. However, ventilation is one of the main ways of controlling exposure to radon daughters. The employer should ensure that if the radiation protection adviser is not fully conversant with the relevant aspects of ventilation engineering then suitable advice is available from someone else.

REGULATION 11
Radiation protection supervisors (RPS)

18 Any person appointed as an RPS should be in a position to exert direct personal supervision of the working practices (see Part 1, paragraphs 81 to 83).

REGULATION 13
Dosimetry

19 The general principles of individual dose assessment as applied to internal and external exposures apply also to exposure to radon daughters. For classified persons such assessments should be made by an approved dosimetry service. Dosimetry relating to persons under a written system of work is subject to Regulation 8(7) (see paragraph 16).

20 Regulation 13 requires that suitable personal dosemeters should be used in preference to a system using area or workplace monitoring and time of exposure. In the unlikely event that the latter method has to be used the employer and his RPA, when making arrangements with an approved dosimetry service, will need to reach agreement on the frequency and places of measurement and an acceptable means of recording to enable the dosimetry service to assess doses. The measurement should enable a realistic estimate to be made for each individual. To achieve this it will be necessary to draw on the existing knowledge of concentrations, the variations in these and the likely movements of the persons involved (see Part 1, paragraph 91). The conditions attached to the approval of the dosimetry service may specify the retention period for the results of area monitoring and time of exposure.

REGULATION 24
Area monitoring

21 The purpose of area monitoring includes determination of the extent of a controlled area or supervised area and demonstration of the effectiveness of control measures as required by Regulation 6.

22 Factors which should be taken into account when determining the frequency for making measurements are:

(a) the likely fluctuation in radon daughter concentrations in a particular place (see also paragraph 23);

(b) the average value of the concentrations;

(c) changes in working practices which significantly alter radon daughter concentrations;

(d) modifications to ventilation systems; and

(e) changes in water flow patterns which could affect the release of radon.

23 Measurements taken should be representative of concentrations in that part or place. Matters which can cause local variations in radon daughter concentrations include the use of compressed air and auxiliary ventilation systems. Fluctuations can also be influenced by both short term and seasonal weather changes. All of these should be borne in mind when measurements are taken so as to determine a representative concentration.

24 Table 1 should be used as a guide to the frequency of measurements. Initial measurements should be taken in any new area of mining and additional measurements should be taken where any change in the control measures or working practices is likely to have altered the previously established levels significantly. When circumstances such as those in paragraph 22(c), (d) and (e) apply it may be necessary to make measurements more frequently than Table 1 indicates.

Table 1

Typical Reading (Working Levels)	Frequency of Measurement
0.03 - 0.05	3 monthly or, if consistent average established, 6 monthly,
0.05 - 0.15	monthly or, if consistent average established, 3 monthly,
> 0.15	at least monthly

25 For mines and other relevant workplaces representative measurements should be taken for all readily accessible places. The number of measurements that need to be taken on each horizon will be dependent on the likely variations throughout

that horizon, the purpose being to obtain a knowledge of radon daughter concentrations and their distribution. In choosing places to make measurements it is important to bear in mind the need to know the levels of radon daughters in those places where persons spend significant periods of time.

Appendix 1

Table of equivalents

The table brings together various numerical requirements of the Regulations and shows the alternative methods of expressing them. For convenience some of the figures given have been rounded.

Requirement	Quantities				
	Dose	Exposure		Concentrations	
	mSv	WLM $Rn222$	$WLM*$ $Practical$	Jm^{-3}	$Working$ $Level$ (WL)
Regulation 5(2) Notification				0.62×10^{-6}	0.03
Regulation 7 Dose Limits	50	4.8	4*		
Regulation 7-Derived Air Concentration					0.3**
Regulation 8(1) Controlled Areas				2×10^{-6}	0.1 (0.096)
Regulation 8(2) Supervised Areas				0.7×10^{-6}	0.03 (0.032)
Regulation 13(3)(f) ADS Notification to the Executive	30	2.9	2.4*		
Regulation 28(1) Investigation Level	15	1.4	1.2*		

* The values given relate to the exposure to radon 222 daughters when additional sources of radiation are likely to be present in the workplace. For most UK situations allowance is thereby made for additional doses from radon 220 daughters, external gamma radiation and internal exposure due to the intake of long lived activity - see paragraphs 10 and 11.

** The figure quoted is based on an exposure for 12 working months in a calendar year and derived from the practical exposure limit.

8

Printed in the United Kingdom for Her Majesty's Stationery Office
Dd289629 3/88 C80 G3379 10170